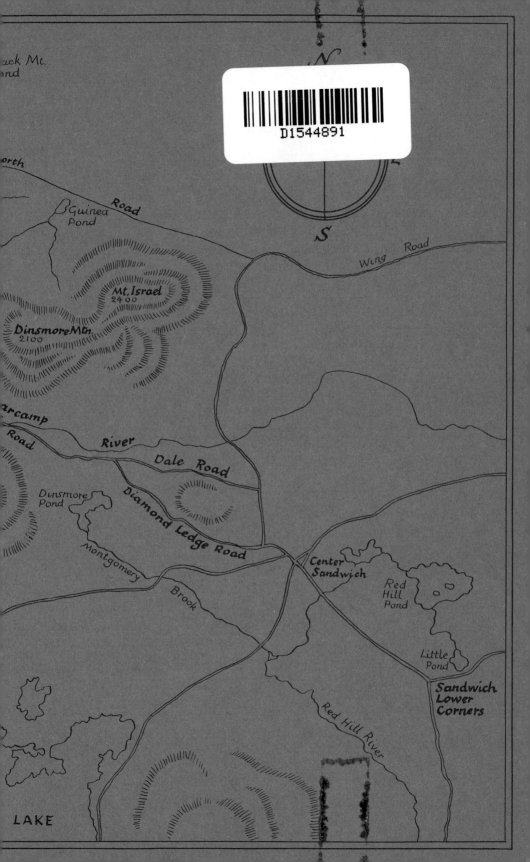

THE ROAD THROUGH
SANDWICH NOTCH

The Notch
road in winter

Elizabeth Yates

THE ROAD THROUGH
SANDWICH
NOTCH

Drawings by Nora S. Unwin

THE STEPHEN GREENE PRESS

Brattleboro, Vermont

This book has been produced in the United States of America:
designed by R. L. Dothard Associates,
composed by Yankee Typesetters, Inc., and
printed and bound by The Colonial Press, Inc.
It is published by the Stephen Greene Press,
Brattleboro, Vermont 05301
Library of Congress Catalog Number: 73-82751
International Standard Book Number: 0-8289-0185-6
73 74 75 76 77 78 79 9 8 7 6 5 4 3 2 1

Through Sandwich Notch the west wind sang
Good morrow to the cotter;
And once again Chocorua's horn
Of shadow pierced the water.

—JOHN GREENLEAF WHITTIER,
Among the Hills

CONTENTS

FOR JOHN DODGE

*who transmitted to me his lifelong affection
for the Notch and its traditions*

THE ROAD THROUGH
SANDWICH NOTCH

THE QUESTION

$\mathcal{I}$T WAS a lovely plan; then a letter changed it all. For months I had been reading about, dreaming about, working toward a pack trip with three friends in the northern Cascade Range. One would come from Minnesota, two from California, I from New Hampshire. Our various flights would converge at Wenatchee, Washington. We would have a day on Lake Chelan, another day or two at a ranch near Stehekin where horses, equipment, and a packer would be obtained; then we would be off for two weeks of high adventure in the virtually roadless area of peaks, passes and mountain meadows.

Letters had been crossing the continent between the four of us ever since we had started our planning, maps had been drawn, our route had been gone over and over, books had been exchanged. By mid-August we were assembling our gear. I had boots and jeans and warm shirts, so my chief purchase had been something called a foul-weather jacket. One of the books had said, "It will be rugged and there will be rain, sometimes day and night, but don't worry, your skin is waterproof." Let it rain, I thought, and imagined myself on a horse over slick trails, drying out by a campfire at night, sliding into a sleeping bag in a tent while rain tapped on the canvas.

The day that confirmation of my flight from Boston to Wenatchee came in the mail there was another letter. It was an appeal to save Sandwich Notch. A map showed a small segment of land on the southerly edge of the White Mountain National Forest and under it was the legend THE LAST MAJOR NOTCH IN NEW HAMPSHIRE WITHOUT SOME FORM OF PUBLIC PROTECTION.

I wondered, What was so important about it that it should be saved? There were more than twenty notches in the White Mountains, narrow passages between two elevations of land. Some of them were well known, like Franconia, Dixville, Pinkham; some were high in the hills and almost unknown. Sandwich was one of the lesser known, but it had a road through it which other small ones did not have. My interest aroused, I read on and discovered that it was the narrow dirt road winding through a wilderness that made it important. For this was no ordinary road, but a road with a history, and one that had helped make history.

Cut through the sparsely settled land in 1801 so
farmers in Vermont and northern New Hampshire
could get their produce to markets, it had, by 1810,
become a commercial highway over which a steady
stream of traffic passed. Carts and wains in the summer, pungs and sleds in the winter came down laden
with wood and wool, cheese, maple sugar, dressed
hogs and hides, tallow and potash; they returned
from the coastal cities, Portland and Portsmouth,
laden with salt and sugar, cotton cloth, glass, store
goods, and barrels of rum from the West Indies. For-
merly such commerce had gone over the Post Roads
or by flatboats down the Connecticut River, but those
routes were longer and they exacted turnpike and
water fees. The road through the Notch was a short
cut that saved time and miles and money. There were
no tollbooths on it. Pedestrians, vehicles, livestock all
could use it freely.

What a marvel of a road, I thought.

There was some further description, mostly of the
scenery as being now "primitive and intimate"; then
came the reason for the appeal. The land through
which the road ran had been under wise and productive timber management for the past fifty years. Now
it had been sold. The threat of development was im-
minent: vacation homes and all that went with them,
wide roads that would give access to ski country, trees

removed so views could be opened up. The last paragraph said:

> *Here is something very real . . . something that New Hampshire has that nobody else in all the world has at this point in time. Sandwich Notch is an opportunity for us to grasp now because, if we do not, it will be gone forever.*

Studying the map, I began to walk the road in my imagination; and soon I was teased by an old memory, a memory of a summer spent at a camp in the White Mountains when I was a little girl. Then, as if a door to a room had opened, something I had not thought about for years came back to me vividly.

One day, six of the older girls had gone with a counselor on a hike that would take them through Sandwich Notch. They had left in good weather, but by noon storm clouds descended and by late afternoon a cold rain fell. The group, expected back for supper, had not returned. When they did, rumbling up in a truck and singing lustily, Taps had already sounded; but we were allowed to leave our bunks and gather at the fireplace in the lodge to welcome the big girls and hear their story. (Remembering, I thought, probably for the first time, with admiration of our camp director: she knew there were times when rules should be set aside.)

One name was on the lips of each of the six girls and the counselor. It was the name of Moses Hall.

The storm had caught up with them when they were halfway through the Notch. They had put on their raincoats and were sloshing along when they came face to face with a man standing in the middle of the road, feet apart, arms folded across his chest. He pointed to his house and said they were to take shelter in it. He would not take No for an answer. Once he had them all in his kitchen, he gave them coffee from a pot on the back of his old wood-burning stove and proceeded to make flapjacks. They were not the only people he had rescued from the storm. A young couple were also there.

One of the girls, as they told of their adventure, kept referring to him as a "sweet, little old bear of a man." Another spoke of his flapjacks as being the best she had ever eaten. Another, that he seemed to want to share whatever he had, his house, his food, his knowledge, his fund of stories: " 'It's yours as well as mine,' he kept saying to us." When they were dry and warm and well fed, he left them to go down to a lumber camp to see about a truck to get them back to camp. It was then that the young couple, in the Notch on their honeymoon, told their story.

They had set up their tent a few days before at a nearby pond. Moses Hall had loaned them the use of his fishing raft and they were having a wonderful time. When the rain came they had taken shelter in their tent, but before long Moses Hall had appeared in the tent opening. "Young man," he said, "this is no place for a woman." Their remonstrance had no effect. He insisted on walking them back the four miles in the rain to his house where the only possible shelter and warmth in all the Notch was in his kitchen by his stove.

After all the stories had been told, the counselor summed the experience up in words that had some-how stayed with me. "Sandwich Notch is a wild sort of place," she said, "but the one man who lives there isn't going to let anyone come to harm in it." It must have been near midnight when we were finally sent to our bunks, and I felt as if I knew someone whose name was Moses Hall. Until I began traveling the road in my mind I had not thought of him for years.

When next I went to the library to return the books about the Cascades, I took out the *History of Carroll County*. I wanted to read about the Sandwich area and see what I could find out about the Notch.

Through all my reading ran the road, or rather a complex of roads that linked an extensive community of wilderness settlements.

The first grant of land in Sandwich had been made in 1763. Two years later Orlando Weed, the settling agent, arrived. The proprietors, to whom the land had been granted and whom he represented, had voted to give him seven hundred acres in any part of the township, also seventy pounds "lawful money" and seven cows. On his part he was to clear forty-two acres, build seven cabins, settle seven families within three years, and remain there himself for six years.

The first settlers, among them Daniel Beede whose name I was often to meet, soon took up their holdings. They cleared land to the north and to the west and far up into the hills. By dint of hard work and persuasive tactics, they extended the size of the township from its original seventy-five square miles to a hundred. Trails were marked by blazing trees—or "spotting" them, as they called it then; fields were outlined with stone walls; roads were laid out as much as possible on high land to avoid the swamps. A cart track went through the Notch to the settlements to the north and the west.

By 1795, as Sandwich became a place of considerable trade, the cart track began to be used more and more. The town appointed a committee to see if it would be practicable to make it a road. Two years later a petition was passed to open such a road, and soon a vote was passed directing that the "Selectmen Petition the Genl. Court for a Tax of Two Cents per acre on all lands in Sandwich for the purpose of opening sd. Road." The sum of three hundred dollars was raised to build a road one rod wide from Sandwich to Thornton.

Then there was controversy.

Many felt that such a road, being a short cut through the township, would be of benefit only to outsiders; others wanted the road laid elsewhere. By 1803 the controversy was sufficiently resolved for the road to be laid and it proved to be as beneficial for the Notch farmers as for the people on the far ends.

Life flourished, land was cleared, some thirty to forty houses were built, each one on high land and anchored against wind by a massive chimney. A gristmill, a sawmill, a still were soon doing business. There was a tavern, and schools. Fields were fertile, orchards bore well, barns were enlarged to care for growing herds of cattle and flocks of sheep. If any amenities were wanted, they could be found at thriving Center Sandwich, a few miles down the road; but Notch folk prided themselves on being self-sufficient.

And now it's a wilderness, I reminded myself. The
farms have gone; the houses have disappeared. How
did it happen?

That night when I went to bed, Sandwich Notch
seemed very near, the Cascades were becoming far
away. Grand and beautiful as I knew they would be,
they did not draw me then so much as did the few
miles of that wilderness road with its quiet and its
memories.

There are times when morning brings more than
light to the world. The next morning was such a time
for me. Without any conscious process of decision-
making, when I awoke and watched the sun rise over
the distant hills, I knew that I was not going to the
mountains of the Pacific Northwest. I was going to
Sandwich Notch to see the road for myself, to walk
its nine-mile length and feel a part of it.

Some letters had to be written, some telephone
calls had to be made, and there was quite a bit of explaining to do. But the choice that had been made
for me was a simple imperative and details fell into
place. I repacked my gear, taking in a rucksack instead of a duffle bag what I would need for a few
days' stay and the walk. I left the foul-weather jacket
at home and cheered my dog's heart with the news
that he could come with me. Gibbie is a Sheltie. He

was named after the character in one of my favorite books, George MacDonald's *Sir Gibbie*. In many ways, particularly that of sensitive companionship, he lives up to his name. Then we were off, early on a September morning, not to a boarding kennel and Wenatchee but to drive a hundred miles due north.

"I thought you were going to the Cascades," my neighbor said, when she stood ready to wave me off.

"Not this time. I'm going to Sandwich Notch."

◆   ◆   ◆

Center Sandwich is a small town in the Lakes Region of New Hampshire, a cozy community. The white houses speak of a simplicity that was once the only way of life and now is, for many, a cherished way. There are spired churches, a store, library, town hall, post office. Gardens were gay with late-summer flowers, there were children playing. I soon found my way to the Historical Society where I obtained some pamphlets; one that had to do with the road through the Notch would, I knew, be helpful. There was a Bicentennial Observance Paper, printed in 1963, which had much useful as well as entertaining information for me. No letters or personal journals of any kind came to light; the Notch folk had been

farming people, apparently too busy living their life
to write about it. But there were any number of
friendly people willing to talk with me about the past
—a treasured past, for it had given meaning to the
present.

There was no one living who had been a part of
the life of the Notch. Over and over again I was told
that the last man to have been born there, and who
had lived there most of his eighty-four years, had died
in 1930. That was Moses Hall. When people spoke
of him I could nod understandingly. I knew something about him, too.

Memories of memories were the past that was
shared with me. I asked questions and listened during
the days spent in the village. Slowly a picture began to
emerge for me, a picture of people against a background I had already established, a background that
covered the years from the 1820's up through the
1880's. Reading had given me a stage; now the stage
had actors. Through words often stark with reality
and as often tender with nostalgia, the drama un-
folded: the drama of daily living.

The people with whom I talked had lived in or
about Sandwich all their years. Most of them were in
their eighties, a few were older. Their memories
spanned the time to the days when the Notch life

was ebbing. It was a fragile bridge, but the mind of an old person can often be clearer with events of seventy years gone than with those of seven days or even seven hours. Reaching back into the past and reliving it, some were grave and of few words; others were possessed by cheerfulness as if the past had been a time of true delight in contrast to the pressure of the present.

The name of Moses Hall was not the only one said often. I grew familiar with that of Doctor Harris and enjoyed the stories about him that some families still cherished. Pastor Meader, the Quaker, was spoken of with respect. No one recalled his sermons but everyone spoke of Pulpit Rock from which he had preached. Schoolmaster Ladd was alluded to by only a few; his time went back to the earliest days.

"When you come to the Devil's Footprints," one man said to me, "see how well they take your feet. Most folks find they can walk right in them."

A woman upon whom I called saw to it that I sat by her fire in her rocking chair. "That was the last chair to come down from the Notch," she said, then went on to tell me that as a little girl she used to take newspapers up to the Notch and come home with a basket of apples. Often in the summer she had taken salt up for the cattle at the Smith farm. Standing by the pas-

ture bars, she liked to listen to the thunder of their
hoofs as they raced down the slope toward her. As she
talked, she rolled something around in her palms and
finally she placed it in my hand. It was a tiny basket,
complete with a handle, hollowed out of a peach
stone.

Peach stone basket

"Moses Hall made that for me when I was a child.
He made them for all the children. He grew the finest
peaches in the Notch."

One man remembered helping his father cut hay
in fields that were beginning to shrink. His grand-
father had been a builder of stone walls, following the
lines made by the surveyors that defined individual
lots. "The range walls go up and over the hills," he
said.

There were others. All spoke of the Notch with
pride, referring to its peaceful, purposeful life as if it

had long ago become part of theirs. In one way or another, each one told me to walk the road and see for myself.

I told them I intended to, for it had been my plan all along to walk the nine miles from east to west and back again, taking two days to do it and spending the night with friends of mine who lived near Campton. It would be an unusual journey, walking in the present to the past; traveling in time that went only forward, traveling in memory that went only backward. I knew that with my eyes I would constantly pierce the green of the surrounding forest as I looked for clearings; with my imagination I would endeavor to create the life that had been where only a cellar hole remained; and with my heart I would long for the impossible—some kind of retrocognitive vision with which I might see events happening long ago as if they were happening now.

BEGINNING OF
THE JOURNEY

*O*N THE MORNING that Gibbie and I set out to
walk the road, the weather forecast promised
something of everything. As if a whole year might be
wrapped up in a day, there would be crispness of
spring in the morning hours, summer warmth as the
day advanced, autumn haze during the afternoon,
and a hint that chill winds would whip down from
the mountains as night came on. The air was indeed
brisk. Dew was on the tall grasses along the roadside.
The sun, just gilding the rounded top of Mount Is-
rael, was glancing off the wooded slopes of Red Hill
across the intervale.

It would be a clockless day. I had no schedule to
follow, no appointments to keep. Without pressure
of any kind, time seemed endless, almost out of pro-
portion to what I wanted to accomplish. The free-
dom I felt was matched only by my excitement at   25

what might open up for me in the hours ahead. All that I needed was in my rucksack; chief among the contents my notebook and pencil, a geological survey map, and a sketch map of the road with numbers indicating sites of former dwellings and landmarks of interest. And I had some food.

The pace I fell into had an easy rhythm, and I found myself swinging along to familiar cadences. Whitman's—

> *Afoot and light-hearted I take to the*
> *open road,*
> *Healthy, free, the world before me* . . .

And Stevenson's—

> *Give to me the life I love,*
> *Let the lave go by me,*
> *Give the jolly heaven above*
> *And the byway nigh me* . . .

And Roethke's—

> *I learn by going where I have to go.*

The Diamond Ledge Road, which I took out from the Center, met up with the Dale Road, also from the Center but not so direct. Where they forked, an-

other road led away and into the forest. A hand-
lettered sign was nailed to a tree. The white printing
and arrow pointing northwest told me all I needed
to know:

SANDWICH NOTCH

Drive Slowly

CAMPTON   THORNTON

This was my road and I took it.

Far off to my right the lowing of cattle from a farm
could be heard. It was a sound that in the old days
must have echoed from one end of the Notch to the
other. The sounds now around me were the chitter-
ing of chipmunks as they played hide-and-seek with
me or each other, the chattering of a small bevy of
chickadees, and an occasional stone dislodged by my
feet. The dirt and gravel road was rough in places,
often rutted, and far more suited to feet or horses'
hoofs than to rubber-tired wheels.

Only the day before I had been told the story of a
low-slung car with an out-of-state license that had
stopped at the post office in Center Sandwich. The
driver was in need of some directions. With road map
in hand, he pointed to the faint line that indicated
the Notch Road and asked if he could get to Campton over it. One of the group of men standing near

by had leaned down and looked under the car. Satisfied that the muffler was only a few inches from the
ground, he straightened up and said to the driver,
"No, you'll have to go around through Plymouth.
That's about forty miles." Mystified or not, the driver
took the Sandwich man's word and went by way of
Plymouth. Now that I was on the road, I understood
the story.

On either side were growing ferns, starred with
late flowers, white and lavender asters, goldenrod.
Behind them were the stone walls, handsome, and in
generally good condition. The first course was boulders that must have been hauled into place by oxen;
the next two tiers could have been brought and laid
by men. Often a single huge boulder filled an entire
space. The trees in the forest beyond the walls grew
tall and extraordinarily straight, among them ash,
oak, maple, beech. Birch were growing near the road,
bending gracefully as birches will and in some places
interlocking their branches to make a canopy of
green. Pines and hemlocks were darker accents of
color. There would be shade, I thought, though it
might be dappled at times, but shade for the length
of the road no matter where the sun might be in the
sky.

September was a lovely time, perhaps the loveliest

of the year. Such stillness rested over the land. Nature was at a pause as the thrust to growth was over. Winter's inwardness was ahead.

The road curved slightly to the right. On my left was evidence of a grassy lane leading up an easy incline. Checking the sketch map, I saw that I was near the Smith farm. This had been a prosperous farm in its day. Where a cellar hole gaped a good-sized house had stood, near by had been the barn. The Smith place was known as one of the most productive in the Notch, with pastures for a large herd of cattle and many sheep, tilled fields, an orchard that yielded five hundred bushels of apples every year and a maple orchard with a yield of a thousand pounds of sugar. The barn had held a cider press; close by had been the blacksmith shop where ox and horse shoes were fashioned as well as tools for work in house and on the farm.

I followed the lane until it became so overgrown with brush and tangled with vines that I would have lost it had it not been for the bordering stone walls. Standing by an opening in the wall on my left, I reflected that a barway had been here, perhaps the very one by which the little girl had stood when she came up from the Center with salt for the cattle. In a shrill voice, she might have called to them, "Bossy! Bossy!"

They might have seen her from a distance, smelled
the salt, and come racing down the slope, their feet
thundering. The story that had been told me made it
all so real.

Squatting on the ground by the bars, she pushed
the chunk of rock salt nearer to them, then she called
them by their names and watched them as they licked
it. Every now and then she held out her hand to be
licked, too, by their rough wet tongues. Did she pick
a buttercup and hold it under her chin for them to
see how much she liked their butter?

Gibbie, exploring on his own, was some distance
from me when I heard him bark. It was not the surprised sound he makes when he inadvertently meets
up with a porcupine, or the startled anguish when
apprised by the action of a skunk. It was a low throaty
questioning sound. Through the trees I could see his
tail wagging. When he returned to me it was still wagging, but more slowly.

"Oh, Gibbie, isn't it a little early in the day to be
seeing things?" I asked, rubbing his head back of his
ears. His Scottish ancestry might help to get him
through the veil of time; but second sight seemed to
me to be more credible at a later hour, not in the
morning's brightness.

I found my way through the woods to the Smith

Smith burying ground

family burying ground, a square clearing surrounded by stone walls. Entrance to it was made between two upright boulders, set with care and just wide enough for those who carried their burden to its resting place in the earth. I knew that I would probably see other such places during my walk but this one was the first and it moved me strangely. I read the names where they were still discernible, and noted the flag that fluttered over the grave of a Civil War soldier. It was a small Stars and Stripes, placed there last Memorial Day and beginning to show a summer's wear. Was this some evidence I was seeking, this grave of a young

Notch man who went to war and did not come back to help his father with the farm, or carry it on in his own name and time?

Back on the road again, it was only a hundred yards or so to a sign on a tree—

BEEDE FALLS

COW CAVE

Finding myself on the map, I realized that this was where the Bearcamp River ran near the road. Names tell stories. In the very early days the six settlers whom I had met in the Carroll County history—including Daniel Beede—made camp on the intervale about a mile downstream from where I was then, and went off to hunt. Returning, they found that a bear had broken into their camp and helped himself to their supplies. The stream received its name from that time on. Beside the road was a parking place where a few cars could be left; a large trash barrel stood under a notice board signed by the Selectmen of Center Sandwich. Among its several advices was the prohibition against using the area after 10 P.M.

A path led through the woods toward the sound of running water. I followed it and came to the falls. There, the Bearcamp River drops over a huge smooth slab of rock into a pool with a sandy bottom. It pursues its way through miniature granite canyons, dropping into clear pools of varying sizes, spreading out over flat rocks, narrowing again to continue its drop until it enters deep woodland and becomes a stream flowing between banks of moss and ferns, shadowed by hemlock and pine. I wondered who had first called it a river, and why. Cow Cave turned out to be a dark, dank hollow created by a great overhanging ledge of granite. I found myself feeling sorry for the cow who had reputedly spent a winter there.

Near the stream there was a sunny place where even the rocks felt warm, a good place to rest awhile. I filled my cup with water and sipped it slowly. The Notch story, all of its hundred years or so, seemed a mere moment in contrast to the geological story that was around me: brief and pastoral one had been, long and tumultuous the other.

Here, as elsewhere in New England, for some two hundred million years great forces had been at work: heat within the earth had thrust molten rock up into ridges, then into peaks. When the glaciers flowed slowly southward, not once but four times, the peaks and ridges were worked upon. Weather continued the shaping with extremes of heat and cold, violent winds. Over more millennia streams were created, valleys carved out, lakes were formed and more rock

exposed. Granite and gneiss were studded with feld-
spar, and gleamed with flecks of quartz and mica, mi-
nute fragments of the fires that had burned within
the earth. Over more aeons a layer of soil built itself
from the débris, a layer that deepened enough to
provide a base for vegetable life. Plants took hold,
then trees. Time measured in thousands of years saw
animate life, and finally man. Then more men, push-
ing their way through the wilderness, clearing it,
making farms and homes.

But the layer of soil was thin, as they were soon
to discover—rich and exceedingly fertile, but thin.
Every year weather continued to do its work as freez-
ing and thawing action thrust rocks to the surface of
the fields. Clearing was an unending task, and never
entirely successful. With each spring the fact became
more apparent that the good soil was wearing away.
Trees held on to it better than crops. Like the flag
fluttering over the grave of the Civil War soldier, the
rocks at Beede's Falls piled up evidence. When news
of better land elsewhere, land that would repay hard
labor, reached the Notch, men went in search of it.

Even back on the road, I was never far from the
sound of water flowing. Along this stretch the Bearcamp River ran near, crossing the road three times at
three different places and giving the section its name

of Three Bridges. Pulpit Rock came between the first and second crossings. My eyes traveled up the wall of granite that rose east of the road and faced west; my thoughts went back to the stories I had read and been told about Pastor Meader.

Pulpit Rock is shaped like the prow of a ship, but a prow blunted by time; in places it is green with moss, in others gray with lichen. At its base are many large stones, stones that look as if they might have been tumbled about long ago by a giant hand. The curtain made by heavy foliage hides much of the rock from easy view, with some of the trees reaching as high as the flat top, while others have taken root on the top with only the soil's thinness to hinder their growth.

Standing there and thinking back to those early years of the nineteenth century when Pastor Meader preached to his people on Sunday mornings, I saw quite easily in my mind's eye the figure of a small man in a broad-brimmed hat standing on the rock, which rose sheer above them and was not yet overgrown. What had they come to hear, those Notch folk gathered up and down the road and among the tumbled stones? What made them leave their farms and walk or ride or drive to this natural sanctuary rather than go the few more miles down to the Center to worship in a proper meeting house? Listening as I stood there, Beginning of it was the whisper of wind in the trees and the run- the Journey ning of water over and around the stones that I heard.

The Bearcamp is one of the headwaters of the Saco River. It has many miles to go to join the larger river, and then more miles before it flows into the sea off the coast of Maine at Casco Bay. Pastor Meader's words were not unlike the river: heard against a background of familiar sounds, heard inwardly again and again as they became part of the larger life of those who listened. Shelley's words were with me then—

O stream!

Whose source is inaccessibly profound,
Whither do thy mysterious waters tend?

Waters of the earth, or those from which if a man drinks he will not thirst again, became one in the forest's stillness.

The road went on and I went with it, calling to Gibbie to stay beside me for a while.

Bracken growing among the aster and goldenrod was a rusty brown. Red berries gave dots of color. A flash of scarlet leaves from a maple just starting to turn stood out against the prevailing green. Even as the landscape spoke of late summer, the reminder of another season was there; not to be taken seriously, but a reminder all the same that winter was not to be taken lightly. The road climbed then went downhill, climbed and dropped again. Reaching the stretch that went by the name of Mount Delight, to walk on the level was a welcome change. The first of the two heights of land had been passed, the one that marked the Saco watershed.

A clearing was here, the first seen since leaving the intervale near the Dale Road intersection. Overhead was the sky, blue with fleecy clouds; ahead was the view to Mount Weetamoo. So long a time I had been under a canopy of green leaves that the feeling of space, the embrace of the sun, were exhilarating. And now the breeze came free across the open land.

A portion of my journey, perhaps as much as half, had been done, and a portion of my day had been expended. The sun looked to me to be approximately overhead and a fairly reliable inner clock told me that it was time for lunch—my meridian meal, as the Notch folk would have called it. There were two cellar holes near the road on either side of the track that led into the field; there might be more if I started really to look and check with the map. I sat down back to trunk with an ancient apple tree that was still bearing fruit, but the small hard apples would be of interest only to deer or a raccoon. Gibbie settled himself

near by, as usual with his tail toward me, and his head
toward the road we had left and from which anything
requiring his attention might come. I offered him one
of his biscuits. He gave me a disdainful look which
said clearly that he did not eat when he was on duty.

The cold milk in my thermos was refreshing, the
sandwich and red apple I had brought with me were
satisfying, and the ground felt good when I stretched
out on it. Grass waved over me and made a green lace-
work through which I watched the flight of a bird
across the sky and followed the passage of clouds.
Herd's grass, they used to call it; in the early days it
grew almost to a man's shoulder.

After a while I walked around the edge of the clearing. Coming to a narrow opening in the trees, I followed a grassy path and soon came to another clearing, one the forest would never take over, for it was a
burying ground, small and looking well cared for. It

was bounded by a stone wall in good condition. No brush or bracken had been allowed to grow up even to its outside edge. Within the enclosure the ground was covered with moss, pine needles and wintergreen. Most of the stones bore words that were easily legible; with a few, words had been erased by weather and lichen. The sun shone into the small area, quiet rested over it; fragrance came from the pine needles.

A few of the stones were slate; most of them were granite blocks, well shaped, with polished tops. The lettering was on the tops, telling names and dates. Walking up and down the rows, I read many familiar Notch names—Bryant, Gilman, Hall. The dates were significant: 1789-1876, that was Jonathan Gilman; and beside him was his wife Sally, 1789-1878. Their lives had spanned the active life of the Notch. Others there must have been more aware of the waning rather than the waxing. There were many small stones for children, and some even smaller for infants. None of the stones was adorned in any way. Notch folk lived and died, their deeds known to those who knew them. Dates told their stories, with no embellishment of weeping willows or winged cherubs.

I thought of an old cemetery down at the Center where the stones told legends of the life. One marked the grave of a five-year-old girl and said,

Her death was accidental.

Another marked the grave of a little boy, dead in 1845 at the age of eighteen months and twelve days. Below the name was the verse—

> *I take these little lambs, said He,*
> *And lay them in My breast.*
> *Protection they shall find in Me,*
> *In Me be ever blest.*

The smallest stone I had ever seen had room enough to say,

> *Beloved daughter, 1 mo., 11 dys.*

There was a feeling of tenderness in the Mount Delight burying place, of intimacy. It was such a short distance across the field from the house that it must have seemed to a grieving family that a unity was still kept. I could imagine a busy mother finding quiet in this clearing, surrounded then by fields and pastures, perhaps coming with socks to knit or beans to shell, perhaps sitting near a small mound and hoping that the next child to be born would stay with life. I could also imagine a young mother with a brood of children and work that was never done coming here in rebellion, stretching herself face down on the earth and weeping because work was unending and there was no escape from it.

But time was on the way to making changes.

The mid-1850's were the watershed for the Notch's life. Events that had shaken the nation reached this small area that had been so largely self-sufficient, so composed, between its mountain ranges. The War Between the States that saved the Union but drained both North and South of many of its ablest young men had taken farm boys from the Notch. Some did not come back; some came only to be laid to rest in the family burying place, and some were drawn West by the lure of good land or gold. Railroads were beginning to reach across the states, then across the continent. A man could go where he had a mind to and be his own master.

News was getting back to the Notch in letters and from travelers about life in the cities where the demand for labor, especially in the factories, was great. Textile mills were busier than ever now that cotton was coming freely from the South. Six days a week at a dollar a day was a tempting wage for a girl; tempting too was the fact that on the seventh day she could do what she liked. On a farm the work was never done and cash money was rarely seen. The young ones, and those without ties, began to leave the Notch as their brothers had done a few years before. The middle-aged worked all the harder, but soon a man sold his flock of sheep, another reduced his herd of cows, and a few fields were taken out of production.

It was not long before it became easier and cheaper to buy store goods from the cities and the produce shipped in from large farms in the Midwest than to make or raise everything needed. Subtly, inevitably, the economy was changing. Small farms, especially those in the hill country, were no longer practical. Walking up and down the short rows in the burying place, reading names and dates, sitting on the stone wall near the boulder that still had in it the iron pins from which a gate had swung, I could see how it had happened.

The clearing at Mount Delight, even though it was no more than a field of a few acres, had given me an indication of the openness that had marked the length of the Notch from Sandwich to Campton, and it had made me aware of the change in its life.

Back on the road, and a short distance along it, I reached the only house still standing—and still inviting, though no one was at home that day. A plain white farmhouse, it was the one lived in by Moses Hall for most of his eighty-four years. There was a plaque on a wall:

JEREMIAH HALL BUILT HERE IN 1826.
THAT HOUSE IS NOW THE WOOD SHED
OF THIS HOUSE, BUILT IN 1877 BY
ALPHEUS MUNSEY HALL.

In the long way of memory, it was Moses Hall who was my link with the Notch, as he must have been with many, hikers or hunters, newlyweds or campers, warming themselves by his stove or sunning themselves on the grass around his house as I had seen a photograph of the Sandwich Historical Society doing on their first Annual Excursion in 1920. Were there not forty-odd years between Moses Hall's tenure on earth and mine, he might appear in his doorway and call out, "Coffee pot's on. Come in and sit a spell."

Gibbie, who had been making a complete survey, returned to stretch himself out in the tall grass beside me. He was satisfied that there was nothing for further investigation, not even a woodchuck hole.

But memories were there, and for me they were a composite of the stories I had been told. Moses Hall had not been the marrying kind, but he had ever had an eye for the ladies and a rough-hewn gallantry when they were present. Hunter as well as farmer, as all Notch men were, he got his deer and his bear every year to provision his larder, and wild fowl as he wished. He could tell, when he would, where the best

trout lurked in any of the ponds from Kiah to the three Halls. As time went on his fields had grown smaller, and time came when he gave up even a pretense of farming; then he worked for the town to keep the road open.

During the summer he cut back brush and repaired the waterbars that kept the road from washing out in the rains; during the winter he broke snow. After a series of storms the snow could lie three feet deep, and clearing it was a heavy task, even for a stout yoke of oxen. More than once the selectmen protested that his bill was too high. He then kept his oxen in the barn and did no more road-opening until he was paid in full. He was past eighty when he moved down to the Center to live with his married sister, but he still chose to spend his days in the Notch, going off each morning with pick or scythe and tied to the handle a packet of food for his noon meal. He died in 1930. When his will was made public, it was known that he left his savings to the town of Center Sandwich. A year later, the Moses Hall Highway Fund of $12,500 was set up for the maintenance of the Notch Road.

Guardian and host of the Notch, Moses Hall left more than a legacy of dollars to his community.

INTERLUDE

*O*N MY WAY again, I realized how sultry the day had become. All of summer's heat seemed trapped within the space that was the road, a green-walled alley. There was no breeze as there had been in the clearing at Mount Delight, no movement of wind through the trees. A sameness had come to my surroundings. Only an occasional cellar hole lay beyond the stone wall; only an occasional gap in the wall indicated where a barway might have opened to a pasture. I had three, or perhaps four, more miles still to go, and for the first time that day the miles seemed long.

The map showed me how close I was to the first of the three Hall ponds, the Upper Pond. They were all small, but the Upper looked larger than the two others, probably some twenty acres or so. The Middle and Lower ponds would best be reached by canoe and I promised myself another adventure, come spring. The way to Upper Hall was little more than a trail, but it didn't seem to be far and though it meant turn-

ing off the Notch Road I decided to follow it. The last
running water had been back some distance. Gibbie
could probably do with a drink.

"Come on, Gib, let's see what's down this way."
We turned to our left and went toward the pond.

Prints in the pebbly sand, much too large and
round for deer, told that moose had gone that way.
Coming around a bend, there was a sharp musk smell
in the air. Bear, no doubt, and within the last few
minutes. I stood still. Gibbie pressed himself close
to me, nose quivering, tail arched over his back. He
knew that, whatever the smell, it was not for him to
pursue.

"Good fellow." I dropped a hand to his head,
fondling him where he liked it best between the ears.

His tail wagged conversationally and we went on.

The more the trail went downhill the stonier it
became, until it turned again and there was the pond.
The long narrow sheet of water was smooth except
for little cat's-paws rippling it where breezes blew.
Oh! how good the light wind felt, for my clothes were
sticking to me and my feet were heavy. Even my rucksack, which had already lost some of its weight, would
be shed gladly.

The sun, becoming hazed, gave the light a translu-
cent quality, made the green wall of Weetamoo on

the far shore look high and protective, gave me the feeling that I had somehow stumbled into another world. I went toward the shore where an old flat-bottomed boat had settled into the water. Another, looking capable of use, stood on its side against some trees. Standing by the water, I reveled in the cooling caress of the breeze on my hot face and damp shirt. It was as refreshing to me as the water that Gibbie was lapping was to him. Hock deep in Upper Hall Pond, he was drinking as if he had never tasted such water before and might not come on it soon again.

A drowsy feeling was coming over me. I didn't feel sleepy so much as completely relaxed. Nothing called

to be done, nothing had to be done that the imme-
diate moment did not provide, and that was enjoy-
ment; outwardly with the touch of the breeze, inwardly with the restfulness that came over me. Bliss.
Peace. I searched for a word to describe the harmony
I felt. I found no single word, but Socrates' prayer
spoke itself within me: *May the inward and the outer
be at one.* I felt it had been answered.

Then I realized that I was not alone.

Sitting on the ground and leaning back against an
old maple tree whose protruding roots reached near
the water, was a girl. She had straight dark hair parted
in the middle and falling over her shoulders, a broad
face with dark brows, high coloring. A smile curved
the corners of her lips; preparation to a greeting it
might be, or intimation of inner happiness. She wore
a loose gray sweater that she might have made herself,
a long wool skirt that she might have woven; her feet
were bare. Beside her was a blanket rolled up and tied
with a strip of leather. She looked so comfortable, so
much as if she belonged, that I felt apologetic for my
intrusion.

"Hello," I said. "I hope I'm not disturbing you."

She shook her head. The smile that had curved the
corners of her lips widened. She opened her hands as
if to offer something. "It's yours too," she said.

Her voice was soft and lyrical, only just strong enough to be heard above the lapping of the water on the sandy shore. Her words, the gesture, the fact that she was the first human being I had seen since the start of the day hours and miles ago back at the Center gave me an exceedingly happy feeling.

"I'm walking through the Notch," I said, "from the Sandwich side to Thornton."

"I'm walking too," she replied, "but the other way."

"Are you camping?"

She nodded and placed her hand on the blanket roll beside her. "Everything I need is with me."

Gibbie, who had drunk his fill, had already found a patch of mixed sun and shade and in it curled up to sleep. He, too, must have felt the pervading peace to relinquish his usual "on guard" attitude. I was glad he had. It made me feel easier about staying by the shore and having a few moments' conversation.

I slid my rucksack off and set it on the ground, then sat down beside it and leaned back against a tree, near enough to be companionable but not so near that the girl could not slip into her silence and I into mine if such seemed the better way for us both. My sense of intruding had gone; in its place was the feeling that we were sharing for a piece of time a beautiful part of the world that was endangered.

Aware of my reason for being in the Notch at all and encouraged by a sympathy in her quiet, I told her why I had come to the Notch.

"And it seems so right to save it," I concluded, "and yet I can't give myself a practical, present-day, dollars-and-cents reason why."

"Surely it's right."

The simplicity of her words startled me. She did not feel required to explain her attitude to herself, as I seemed to feel I had to explain mine. Apparently she could accept what was right as right and leave it at that.

"I've read what I could find about the Notch life," I went on, "I've talked with people whose memories go back a long way, but there must be ever so many more stories."

"Oh, there are indeed, as many as leaves on a tree." There was laughter in her tone. "Some go one way, some another, like the one about the cow who spent the winter in the cave near Beede's Falls."

"You know some of the stories then?"

"I do. I've been told them."

"Tell me about the cow."

"There's not much to the story about the cow; there's more in it about the Notch people. She strayed from her pasture. Cows were always doing that and often they weren't missed for several days. When she was missed, it was too late to go in search of her, for winter had set in. The cow found a shelter for herself, trust a Notch cow to do that, near the falls under that overhanging ledge. Moisture drips from the cracks so she had the water she needed, and there was browse close by so she had only to step out or, if the weather was not clement, thrust her head out to get what she hungered after. It was that way she spent the winter. When she was found in the spring, some said she was none the worse for her experience and some that she was dead."

"Is it true?"

"It's a story. Who can say what's true? You take what you like, the way you take a strand for your weaving and work it into your cloth."

"What did you mean when you said the story told more about the Notch people than about the cow?"

"That there are some who look on the dark side while others look on the light. Isn't that true of people everywhere?"

"Yes, of course. What do you think happened to the cow?"

"She lived! She lived indeed, and when the time came right again she was bred to the fine red bull

that was brought to the Notch from Holland. Later
on, when she birthed a calf it was one of the best of
the Notch cattle, and red, redder than her sire."

I asked her more about the farms, and answering
me her words fairly tripped over themselves with
eagerness. It was clear that this was where her heart
was. I wondered what one of the Notch families she
was descended from and intended to ask her.

"As soon as the clearings were burned over, lean-
to's were built; but they were not lived in for long.
A man had all the wood he needed to build his house
and that was what he wanted for his family. Houses
were set on high land for the best of reasons: more
hours of sunlight in a day, more weeks of growing in
a year. Early frosts in May and September shortened
the season in the valleys, but they were unknown on
the hilltops. The new land gave heavily. What a man
did not raise on it for food, or with his own stock, he
found in the woods, for game was plentiful. Most of
the farms had ten head of cattle, though some had
more, and at least forty sheep. Their small sharp
noses could find grazing among the rocks while cows
needed good pasture. There were oxen and horses,
hogs and chickens, animals that helped with the work
and those that supported life. There was always a
skep or two of bees for pollination, with their honey

for sweetening and their wax for making candles.''

She paused for a moment, half closing her eyes, as if she were seeing it as she had been told about it.

"From the forest a man had the wood he required to keep his house warm in the winter, to make its furniture when he had time to fashion it, tables and chairs as well as cradles and coffins, tools as well as trinkets. Everything you can think of was made from

Heart of the Notch

wood, though some things were of iron and shaped in a smithy. There was more than one such in the Notch. And a woman had what she needed in her garden to feed her family and clothe them with flax for her loom, and wool from the sheep. But she had few pretties, except as her man could make them from things that were at hand.''

"Did they have any books?''

"In a few houses there were some, but there was one in every house. The Bible. It was used to record births and deaths and marriages, and it was read from often."

"It must have been a hard life."

"Not to them," her face gentled with a smile; "it was life."

The picture she outlined appealed to me. In spite of the demands made on physical strength, it sounded like an idyl. I longed to slough off my twentieth-century ease and be back in the early days of the Notch. I said as much.

"Aye, hardship did indeed make them strong." There was a ring of pride in her voice. "And the difficulties they faced made them ever thinking toward new ways of doing things. It's fine for a man to see the work of his hands around him, a woman her skill. With a place they had made for themselves, they were subject to no one. Work was never ending, but their lives depended on it; and every member of a family did a share, the old ones and the children too. Women made the butter and cheese that went to market, and the soap; they plucked the geese and wove the coverlets and twisted into baskets the withes that the children had found."

"They must have been happy."

"If they found happiness first in themselves, they
could let the lave go by."
"The lave?"

She had turned her head away and either did not
hear or did not heed my question. I did not really
need a reply, for I knew what she meant. It was what
Stevenson meant in the poem that had sung itself
within me more than once that day—

> *Give to me the life I love,*
> *Let the lave go by me . . .*

When you have what you love: a companion with
whom to share life, a shelter from the weather, work
to do that needs doing, and beauty at your door; it
doesn't matter what you don't have. The rest—or that
lovely old word, the "lave"—can go by.

We were both silent for a while; she, with her gaze
across the water, I with my eyes closed, the better to
see into another way of life.

When she spoke again, her voice sounded as if it
were coming out of a dream and her tone had
changed. Looking at her, I saw that she was shaking
her head. "Winters were long and rigorous. Snow
came early and shut people off from the world, often
from each other. Sometimes it shut them into themselves. It was hardest on the women, hungering for

someone to talk with, longing for the sight of another woman. The men could go hunting, and there was always the tavern where rum flowed like water. But a woman was kept home. She might lift her eyes to the mountains she saw from the small panes of her windows and wonder what lay beyond them. Blue and beautiful as they might be, outlined sharply against the sky, they were the unassailable wall. On the other side of them was the unknown; on her side, what had been and would always be. Winter was a dour time for many."

Her voice drifted away. I felt there was still much she could tell me but I did not want to press her for more than she was willing to share.

After a while she asked me if I had come by Master Ladd's house.

Reaching into the rucksack for my map I opened it and spread it flat on the ground, moving two stones to hold it in place. I nodded. She was obviously referring to a cellar hole, one of the many I had not actually stopped to explore but had come by.

"Did you note the trees?"

I wondered which trees she meant of the many crowding up to, and growing out of, every cellar hole. I could only shake my head.

"Don't fash yourself," she laughed. "You can't see

Balm of Gilead

everything. The trees I'm speaking of are the Balm of Gilead. Some think that's a poplar, but it is not. Notch folk often planted them by their houses for the music in their heart-shaped leaves. Master Ladd knew about such things."

"He was a teacher, wasn't he?"

"The very best. But he wasn't the only one, for there were three school districts in the Notch."

"Three!" It was difficult for me to imagine the need for so many on a nine-mile stretch of road.

"With more than thirty families living hereabouts there was a throng of children to start on the road to learning." She chuckled. "Some didn't get very far, but at least they got started. When there was no school building, school kept in a farmhouse; but there wasn't a Notch man unwilling to tax himself for a school and to work on the building of one."

"But three! Where were they?"

"At the near end and the far end of the road and at Mount Delight. They saw a heap of living, those schools, and not just learning. They were gathering places for meetings of all kinds—husking bees and apple parings, singing festivals and spelling bees. Folk walked to them barefoot in the summer, on snowshoes in the winter. When snow didn't block the road altogether, they'd get to the gatherings by sled."

"What about the children who went to school?"

"They walked, most of them, and the way the schools were placed no one had more than a few miles. The bairns from the Smith farm rode. Colonel Smith had an old white horse, as trustworthy as she was sure-footed. On school mornings all three of the little ones would be lifted on to the mare's back and up the hill she would take them to the doorstone of the schoolhouse, then she would turn around and go back to her pasture. She knew when it was time to fetch them and would wait at the pasture bars for Colonel Smith to let them down for her. It was no longer than it takes to go up and down that bit of road before she had them safe home again.

"One day"—her tone shivered with disgust and her expression changed—"a stranger walking over the road met the white mare and thought she was lost. He turned her around and sent her down the hill where he thought she belonged." Stopping abruptly, she made her hands into fists as if she would have given that stranger more than a piece of her mind. "People should not interfere with the Notch folk."

"Weren't you going to tell me something about Master Ladd?"

"Aye, that's what I was about to do! There were many teachers through the years, some came from the Center and boarded with one family or another the eight weeks in the summer and the eight weeks in the winter that school kept; some came from even farther away. They were paid well, one dollar and fifty cents a week, and their board was free. Master Ladd lived in the Notch. He was born here and he never went away. He was a man of large comprehension, indeed he was."

"Master Ladd," I repeated. The name had charmed me when I first came upon it in my reading.

"He was lame, but what need had he of legs when his mind could go round the world and his words could take the children with him?" Her tone became wistful. "Perhaps that was why some of them, when they grew up, began to leave the Notch. They had learned there was more to the world than the space between their mountains, but I doubt if they ever found there was more to life.

"One of the schools was not far from the Ladd house. Every morning during the summer weeks the big boys took turns drawing a wagon they had made up to the doorstone and helping Master Ladd into it, pulling him to the schoolhouse; in the winter they made the journey by sled. But there was no school for anyone once snow blocked the road.

"There was often trouble in the other school districts, for there were boys with no mind to learn who had nothing better to do with themselves than break windows and cause trouble, and more than once a schoolhouse was set on fire; but not where Master Ladd taught. He seemed to know what the young ones needed and that it was not always to be found in books."

"How long did he teach"

"A long time. It was his life."

I was remembering something I had recently read. When settlers had made their land workable and built their own cabins, then houses, next to be built

was a meeting house for worship and a school for
learning. A tavern followed and with the three there
was a town. I spoke of this.

"But the Notch was never a town. It was a neighborhood."

"As well as a way of life?" I asked.

"Aye," she nodded. "You may be right."

"Thank you for telling me about Master Ladd. I'd read about him, and I've been told about Doctor Harris and Pastor Meader. There were many great people living in the Notch."

"Good people," she corrected. "And you ken Moses Hall?"

Her use of the unusual word did not startle me so much now as it had earlier, but it slowed my answering. "Ken? You mean, did I know him?"

She nodded.

"I did not know him, only of him."

That seemed to satisfy her, for beyond reminding me that I had come by his house she said no more about him but went on to talk about Doctor Harris. "You passed his house, too."

Finding it numbered on the map, I realized that it was another one of the cellar holes in the woods on the other side of the stone walls that ran along the road. Many of them I had passed without taking any particular notice. She was making me aware that in missing the site of a house I was also missing something of the life that had been lived at that particular spot. I wasn't going to fash myself about my negligence, but I had a feeling that when I retraced my steps tomorrow my mind's eye would be sharper than my eyesight.

"Doctor Harris had a large family and all of them were boys. He was a seventh son. One of his own was a seventh son and they all say he had the gift of second sight, but of that I know nothing. Doctor Harris spent his eighty years in the Notch, and most of them were in the practice of medicine. One of the sons lived on in the old place long after every one else near him had gone. The spring from which they drew their water flows as it always did. It's there for any thirsty person to drink from, and the wild creatures know it well.

"There was not much sickness, for once people grew out of childhood they lived long, but there were accidents. And there were troubles for which neither cause nor cure could be found. Stomach ailments were common, but Doctor Harris had his own remedy for them. It was a mixture of burdock seeds, poplar bark, and gum aloes pounded with a pestle in an iron mortar. The powder was then steeped in

alcohol and taken in cold water. Bitter!" She made a
face as if she had once tasted it.

"And it didn't make them sicker?"

"It made them well!" she exclaimed indignantly. "Most of his remedies came from herbs, and the trees. Some he had learned from Indians. Some he discovered and used first on himself. He was a great one for applying spider webs to stop a flow of blood, and he always said there was nothing like mold on bread for certain ills. Apple trees bore well in the Notch and he told people something easily remembered, 'Eat an apple before going to bed and you'll make this doctor beg for his bread.' Ah, he was a man of mirth too, he knew people needed laughter. But there was nothing he, or anyone, could do when a man was gored by an ox, or bitten by a mad dog, or when a woman grew so thin that she was only skin and bones."

"There was no insurance in those days," I reflected.

"Just being careful."

"There must have been times——" I began.

As if she had caught my thought she interrupted, "Oh, there were, times when a man would be working in the woods and for all his care something would go wrong and the tree he was axing went on him before it went to the ground. When the cold got a man, as it did James Bryant, there was no hope either."

"What happened to James Bryant?"

"He was on his way back from the Center where he had gone to get supplies, one winter day. Wind lashing snow before it swept down from the hills and he could not see to goad the oxen past the great rock near the turning to Asahel Wallace's intervale. As deafened by the storm as he was blinded, the oxen did not hear his call to halt but plodded on with the pung and reached their barn. When the family saw that James was not with them, his sons followed the tracks and came to what was their father, frozen stiff near the side of the rock, half buried by snow. There was nothing that could bring the life back to him, not fire on a hearth or the fire of rum within. Notch folk rarely passed judgment on their own, but there were those who said James Bryant should have trusted his beasts. They have their own ways of knowing. But, 'Death comes to us all,' Doctor Harris would say, and because he had kept it from them when he could or helped them face it when no more could be done, his words carried comfort."

"How do you know all this?"

"I've been told. I remember."

Her eyes reminded me of Gibbie's when I question something reasonable to him but puzzling to me.

"There were things Doctor Harris could not have done without rum," she added; "it helped in many ways."

I judged there had been no lack of it.

She went on to tell me how the wains that had gone through the Notch from the west brought rum back from the coast to the settlements. "And the men made themselves merry on the journey, often stopping to open a bung and have a sip or more than a sip; but it lightened the load that made the beasts strain up the long hill to Benny Durgin's tavern where some of the barrels were rolled off. But whether they were going east or west, there was always a hill to climb, for the tavern was situated between the two heights of land and stood at a place where the road ran level. Men were glad for its cheer, and the beasts were ready to stand in the big barn for a while or graze in one of the pastures."

I glanced down at the map to locate it. Her voice was like a pointing finger. "You've already passed the place. It's where the Notch Road is joined by the North Road, but you'll see it on your return."

Finding it on the map, I tried to see it in my mind as I listened to her.

"A bonny big place it was and in it there was always room. If the beds were full a man could throw his blanket down by the hearth and sleep there. Food was plentiful—potatoes roasting in the ashes, a bannock of oatmeal baking on a maple chip, and bean porridge. There was a fire on the hearth cold days or hot. If it was not needed for cooking it was needed to keep the loggerhead ready for the flip."

"Loggerhead? Flip?"

She smiled, tolerant of my ignorance, and explained as if to a child that a loggerhead was a long-handled tool with a bulb on the end. It was kept warm in the coals. When thrust into a mug of spiritous liquor the result was called a flip. But a toddy was what they called for in the winter, because men said it warmed them twice: once when lips touched it and again when heat got into the veins.

"Rum was for those who could pay the price, but many of the drovers got their comfort from beer made of pumpkin and apple seeds mixed with bran, or whiskey made from potatoes. They were abundant, for potatoes grew well on the Notch land. Six cents a mug a man paid for his flip, and six cents for two quarts of oats for his horse if it was stabled for the night. A team cost more, eight cents for a whole baiting of hay. Ready money was not come by easily and often a man paid for what he received in salt."

"Salt was as precious as that?"

"Indeed it was, for it came from the coast and it was in much demand. How would a Notch man cure hides for boots and britchen and harness without it? How would a Notch woman pickle the pork or the eggs without brine? And the stock had need of it. Without a salt lick at home, cows took to wandering in search of one. Aye, salt was good money."

"When did the drovers come through?"

"Twice yearly, spring and fall, driving the cattle from the coast to summer grazing in the hills, and driving them back again. It was easier then to get cows to the hay than hay to the cows. In the spring they were scrawny and skittish; in the fall they were sleek and slow-moving.

"Notch folk never knew the day the drives would come through, but they announced themselves. The distant thud of their hoofs was like rain in the forest before it advances across the fields. A shuffling came nearer and nearer, the sound made by hundreds and hundreds of hoofs on the road. Mingling with it were shouts of men, barking of dogs, bellowing of cattle. When the herd came into sight there was nothing to be seen from stone wall to stone wall but the brown bodies of the beasts, lean and shaggy from the winter. In haste to get where they were going, they tossed their horns and thrust out their noses as if they could smell what was ahead for them.

"People stopped what they were doing to see the great sight—women hanging out their washing or churning butter, men planting gardens or splitting wood, all stood still to watch the procession pass. Children climbed trees the better to see, and there wasn't a boy who didn't want to be a drover when he became a man. Such waving and shouting had not been heard in the Notch for a year, but voices of men were lost in the scuffling and braying. If the season was a dry one, there was not much to be seen for the clouds of dust that rose from the road.

"Men saw that their pasture bars were up and in place for they didn't want cattle from the coast mixing with their own herds, but sometimes the beasts pushed aside each other and went over the walls, knocking down stones, so tempted were they by the good green Notch grass. Dogs rushed in after them barking. Men swung their birch switches and yelled 'Git out o' there! Git along wi' you!' But if something held the drive up and it was late, or if a storm came on, the Notch men had holding places where the cattle could bide while their own were put out to pasture. Some thought that all the cows in the world

were in the Notch at the time of a drive; others,
more used to numbers, called it a thousand head.

"The drive that came down in the fall was different. The beasts were fat and in prime condition. They moved at their own pace, they mooed contentedly. Many of them would go to markets in the cities on the coast; many that were breeding stock would go back to their farms. As far as the eye could see, up one long hill and down another, the brown tide flowed. A wagon or two brought up the rear. In it were the little calves that had been born up in the pastures. Some of them jumped out and ran to find their mothers when the herd stopped to drink at one of the streams along the way.

"If school was not keeping, and even if it were, Notch boys were given leave to walk along by the drovers and their dogs. Asking questions, they listened to stories and learned a new lingo as they did. Often they went as far as the coast, slept in the hay at taverns, and came back filled with their own stories of the world they had seen. They were different from that time on for they felt like men. They knew there was a place for them in the world of men and they were restless. It was hard for the girls. Their hearts might be drawn out of them to the venture beyond, but their places were at home."

Remembering how high Pulpit Rock had seemed when I passed it, I wondered if many a small boy had not watched the passage of the cattle from its height, able to catch the first glimpse of tossing heads over the brow of the near hill to the last sight of switching tails down the far hill.

"Did you note Pulpit Rock as you came by?"

"Indeed I did. I walked around those huge stones at the base where the Bearcamp runs and I looked up the rock to see what I could of the sky."

"Do you ken what Pulpit Rock meant in the life of the Notch?"

"Only that a Quaker pastor used to stand on its height and preach from it."

"Only!"

The way she said the word made me sorry that I had used it.

"The Meader farm was on the land above the river. It's a steep climb from the road up to it and a braw place it was, open to the sun but sheltered on the northeast by rising hills. The higher you went from the house and barn the more you could see of the world." Then she shook her head slowly.

It was a gesture I had grown used to because she did it frequently when speaking. It seemed to convey a particular mood, not of melancholy so much as

acquiescence. "You'd see nothing but trees from
there now," she added.

"I know. It was all I could do to get a glimpse of
sky through the greenery."

"There were many Quakers in the Notch, but Jo-
seph Meader was the one who had the gift to preach.
He could say words in such a way that they went
from mind to heart and took root in people's lives.
He had gone from the Notch to get his book learning, but he returned to use it with his own. He spoke
in a way that people could understand and he spoke
about what they knew. Often, perhaps it was always,
he spoke of the beauty and wonder of the world that
was theirs right where they were living. He made
them feel themselves to be a part of it all.

"From the door of his house he would go down the
path to the Bearcamp, cross it, and climb up the
nearest high rock. There he had a pulpit from which
to preach. In clement weather people came from up
and down the Notch, on foot, on horse, in wagons
drawn by oxen. They sat on the rocks near the
stream, on the walls along the road, even up the
hillside. His voice was powerful, and the surrounding rocks may have helped to send it forth. Even the
old ones whose hearing was failing never lost a word
of what he said, and the little ones wanted to listen."

Pulpit Rock

"Didn't people ever go down to the meeting house at the Center, or to the one in Thornton?"

"Why should they when they had Pastor Meader?"

"Did he write his sermons?"

She shook her head, but not vigorously. "That I would not know but I would doubt. He was a Notch man with fields to till, beasts to care for, and a family to feed. People remembered and passed his words on, one to another."

This was the answer she had given me before in somewhat similar words, and probably would again. I wanted to ask her what would happen when memory faded altogether or when the slender strands that held it were dissolved by time. I did not, feeling that I would not get a satisfying answer. Instead, I asked her what happened when the weather was not clement.

"They came to his house and sat near the fire of logs on the hearth. Sometimes they filled the room from one wall to another. But once winter settled down, it closed life in and Notch folk had to tell each other in their own homes what they recalled of the sermons heard from Pulpit Rock. Winter could be long, often from December until April, then it took time for the mud to dry so the roads would be open for travel. I've been told that winters would have

seemed longer had it not been for the thoughts Pastor Meader had given to tide them over. A woman
working at her loom, a man fashioning tools, did better with good things to think about."

"I wonder what he said, what he did, that made
his words take such hold."

"I'll tell you what he said and how he said it, for
it's been told me often." She paused and looked
away from me across the water, then her words came,
slow and deliberate words.

"He would come out on the rock at the appointed
hour and stand quite still. He was a small man and
his broad-brimmed hat shaded his face. There he
would stand, as if he cared not how long, until the
people who had gathered became still too, the bairns
in their mothers' arms, the children at play, the men
in the clothes they wore only on Sundays.

"He asked them to listen, to go back to the days
when they first came to the Notch. What did they
hear? No one of those men and women was likely to
forget the sounds of the wild—the scream of a pan-
ther, the bark of a bear, the howl of a wolf. In time
the air filled with other sounds: axes chopping, trees
falling, saws grating, and the hammering that echoed
from hill to hill as houses were built. And that summer morning, near and far were the sounds of a

good life, humming of bees, mooings and bleatings, whinnyings and cacklings. As they listened, the bells on hundreds of Merino sheep tinkled through the air. That was a way he had of bringing them up through the years."

"What a way!" I exclaimed, in reverence as much as admiration.

"Pastor Meader never expected people to give him an answer when he took them journeying in this fashion. He wanted them to go on listening to all that spoke to them in ways they could understand. When he ceased his words, he stood still again, and again as if it did not matter to him how long he stood there. The quiet was friendly, only the sound of leaves in a near tree and water running in its course marked it. I've been told that what Pastor Meader wanted most of all was for them to hark to the silence that was within each one and in that silence sift their thoughts. It was not what had been good in the week just passed, or what had been wrong that mattered greatly, it was what had meaning for each one. He helped them to care about what happened in themselves, for a man who took care for himself was more apt to be careful of others."

"That was preaching!"

"It was his way. Do you wonder now that the

Notch folk did not go down to a meeting house?
Why hear a dour preacher say that the good life was
waiting them in heaven when they died? They had
it in the Notch while they lived. 'Let heaven come in
its time,' Pastor Meader used to say."

"You might have been one of those who heard
him."

"I've heard tell about him." Her eyes were wide
with honest assertion.

When she spoke again her words carried another
kind of emphasis. Apparently she wanted to be sure
that I did not hold a one-sided view of Notch life.

"Pastor Meader knew that living was neither easy
nor always happy," she went on. "There had been
sorrow in his own household, and indeed what house
in the Notch did not know sadness at one time or
another? Often it was not that which comes to us all
in time, but that which was cruel and hard to understand. There were women unable to abide the sight
of the house and the man they were bound to who
took matters into their own hands. There were men
who suffered loss with their stock—lightning killing
a herd sheltering under a tree, a sow newly farrowed
and rolling over on her sixteen piglets so that no one
of them breathed again; there were those who took
to rum and made the bottle their life; there were in-

fants born imperfect who spent their lives hidden away by their parents or in useless gawking at others; there were———" the recital she clearly did not enjoy ended abruptly. "But these happen anywhere, not in the Notch alone."

"No, not in the Notch alone, and not only in the nineteenth century."

"Pastor Meader used to comfort them by saying that the world learned by its mistakes, as people did, and that a time would come when life would be better than it was then. For many, this was hard to believe; to them, it was good as it was."

The sun had lowered considerably during my time by the pond. Resting my eyes on the path of light across the water, I thought how much like that quivering line were memories as they brought the past to life and lighted the future.

"See that path that leads to the base of Mount Weetamoo?" I pointed to the light. "That's what your stories have done for me: made a link with another time."

She followed my gesture with her eyes. "So they call it Weetamoo now? That's one of the Indian names. In the days of the Notch, folk always called it Catamount."

"Why?"

"Because a hunter's dog treed a catamount some-
where on that rugged trailless slope."

"A little like the cow at the falls?" I asked.

Her lips curved into the smile that had captivated me at my first sight of her. "Aye. Believe as much as you like."

We were silent then, both of us resting our eyes on the path of light that rippled and shimmered across the pond.

"You have a long way to go," she said, calling me back to my present.

"Yes," I agreed, but somehow I did not think she meant the road. "I've been a long way, into another time, another life." Then I told her of my sadness at the way the Notch life had gone so utterly, leaving almost no trace.

She raised her arms in a sweep that embraced the lake, the mountain, and me. "There are a few more hours of light left in this day. Each one of us will use them to go our ways. Will you be sorry to see this day take its leave?"

I shook my head. "It's been a beautiful day. I can keep it in my memory as perfect. And there will be tomorrow."

"Even so." Her words came like an Amen. "The life of the Notch went when it had had its day. It lives on in tales told long ago but remembered. And there is tomorrow, for the Notch as for us."

"How did it go?" Even though I knew, it seemed important to have her answer.

"Gradually." Her tone was matter of fact. "The soil was thin, it soon wore out and was good for neither pasture nor tillage. Sons went to war and did not return; daughters married and went away to live. News of good land in the West drew other young men away; news of good money in the factories drew young girls to the cities. Change was in the air and with it there was restlessness. In time only the old folk were left and when life got too hard for them they moved down to the Center, taking a few of their cherished belongings and leaving the lave."

How tender she is with that word, I thought; almost as if asking forgiveness.

"And the houses were abandoned."

"Unoccupied," she corrected me. "They were dismantled and what could be used again was taken elsewhere. A house without windows soon lets in the weather, a roof with rotting shingles soon sags; and once the frame weakens the house itself goes tumbling into its cellar. Beyond, where fields had been bounded by walls, brush took over. Barways

disappeared. Stones were toppled from walls. It was
slow at first, then it went fast as the forest took back
what was its own."

All during our conversation I had been the one to
question her, now she put a question to me. "What
can one do when the end comes to a way of life? to a
day?"

Her quiet reasonableness must have had its effect
on me for all I could say was, "Accept it, and look
ahead."

She nodded.

The Notch life had rounded its growth in a little
more than a century, but its people had lived in
their present. Something that could no longer be
maintained had been let go, and it had gone as nat-
urally as the ebbing of the day. There had been no
decline, only change. What would Pastor Meader
have done with that? I wondered. But perhaps from
the height of Pulpit Rock he had seen it coming and
had prepared them as he charged them to live in the
day and let heaven come in its time. I folded the map
and tucked it into my rucksack, then I stood up.
Gibbie shook himself out of sleep and came to stand
beside me.

"You've made the Notch real to me, and I thank
you."

"It's yours," she said. Her voice was as soft as the light wind in the maple leaves above her, as murmurous as the water lapping the shore. I might have lost her words altogether had they not been familiar to me.

Turning away, I started up the trail that would take me back to the Notch Road. It rose steadily. When it veered to the right I was tempted to look back for one last glimpse of sunlight shimmering on water, for one last wave of the hand. But I didn't. I was not sure that she would still be there.

So I returned to the present, feeling that some true touch with the past had been established. Gibbie trotted ahead of me eagerly. I walked more slowly, dislodging a stone now and then but not stumbling as I had when I came down that same incline. The time, however long it had been, had refreshed me. There were still a few more miles to go, but now I would do them easily.

CONTINUATION OF
THE JOURNEY

*M*UCH OF the way was downhill. Near the western end of the road I passed a small dwelling that had once been a schoolhouse. Set well back from the road, surrounded by trees, it was quite clearly serving another purpose. Summer home? hunting lodge? Whatever it was now, it was well cared for. One of the three schools in the Notch had been called the Jefferson School. It might have been this one. The name, of course, recognized the forty voters in the Notch, all of them Democrats, who cast their ballots religiously in town, state, and national elections. In later years there was known to be one Republican, who also cast his ballot as the different elections came along. This would have been after the War Between the States, or the Civil War as it came to be called.

When I emerged from the woods, it was to follow

the road through open fields and an apple orchard. There was a comfortable white farmhouse on one side, a weathered gray barn on the other. This was what the road must have been like, all its length up hill and down from Sandwich to the end which I had all but reached. Standing still for a moment and looking around me, I took in the spaciousness of the view, little different for me in my day from what it had been for the Notch people in theirs.

The long ridge on my right culminated in Sandwich Dome. The long ridge on my left cut off the view to Osceola, but not Tecumseh which rose on the west across the Mad River. As Catamount had been changed to Weetamoo, so with many of these peaks; the names were being changed from the descriptive ones given by the early settlers to those reminiscent of Indians.

Beyond and in a northerly direction was the vast expanse of the White Mountain National Forest. Looking east of north was the Presidential Range culminating in the great mass that was Mount Washington, though this was not to be seen from my viewpoint. Letting my eye reach and range over the peaks and ridges and density of trees that made up the National Forest, I felt a surge of pride: this land was protected, managed, for people to use and enjoy for ever. It was *their* land. My land. Then, counter to the surge was a twinge of another emotion. The land I stood on and had been part of for a day, and would return to tomorrow, was endangered. It might not always be wild and free unless enough people cared enough to keep it so; to save it as the National Forest had been saved.

The sun, directly before me, was balanced on a distant range. I waited to watch it go from sight, then took my jacket from my rucksack and put it on, glad for its warmth. The breeze that had been welcome by the lake had now become a wind that was cold and searching.

"Come on, Gibbie."

We started ahead again, for though we had come to the end of the Notch Road, we were not at the end of our adventure. I walked fast, which pleased Gibbie. It was not far to the friends' house where we would be spending the night; but darkness comes swiftly in the mountains.

◆　　　◆　　　◆

The next day could hardly have been said to dawn, the light merely changed through shades of gray. Clouds hung low, obscuring the mountains. The air was damp. My hosts, who sent me on my way with

food in my rucksack for a noon meal, assured me
that there was no rain in the low-hanging clouds,
"Though there may be no clearing either."

I was glad for the change in the weather. It would
make everything different. Retracing my steps as I
would be, the road would not be the same. Sunshine
and frolic breezes giving place to mist and quiet sent
the hills back into themselves; a little the way the
life of the Notch had retreated into itself when the
forest reclaimed the land. A secret was in the hushed
air, but it was a secret to which I was rapidly becoming privy and one that I knew I would want to share.

Walking along and humming in time with my
stride, the words that began to sing themselves in
me were Robert Bridges'—

> *I made another song,*
> *In likeness of my love:*
> *And sang it all day long,*
> *Around, beneath, above:*
> *I told my secret out,*
> *That none might be in doubt.*

Whatever the weather was or might be, this day
was mine, hour after unhurried hour. Not sun but
hunger would tell me when it was nearing midday;
tiredness when it would be good to rest.

Silence enclosed me, dissipated occasionally by

moisture forming on leaves above and slipping
down to leaves below, or by an acorn dropping with
a thud. The ferns that grew along the stone walls
drooped wetly. My map told me of the cellar holes I
was passing and I imagined the living that had gone
on at each one. It was easier to do this now. The
hour at the pond that brought memories alive had
made people real, their situations actual.

The turning off the road to the pond did not draw
me. I was feeling fresh and cool and in no need of a
halt; and I knew my friend would not be there.
Where she had gone mattered as little as where she
had come from. She had been there when I had appeared and for a period of time our lives had over-
lapped. Somehow it had not seemed to matter who
we were, so we had remained nameless. I supposed
that her people had been one of the families from
Scotland who had been early settlers in the Notch,
for her conversation had been salted with Scottish
words. Why hadn't I asked her name and where she
lived? It had been my intent to, but I had kept for-
getting.

A cellar hole rimmed with popple growth told of
fire, for popple invariably followed burning in field
or near a dwelling. Another drew me to exploration,

for it was that of the Durgin Tavern. The granite sills were still solidly in place, the doorstone was massive. When hauled there, that block of granite must have strained the muscles of at least two yoke of oxen. Far too heavy to be dragged away by any later-day person searching for something to put into a new house, it had remained. The crumbling bricks of the chimney spoke, too, of size. Built to hold the house in defiance of storms or earth tremors, it had not been able to defy time. I picked up a piece from a brick and put it in my pocket as a talisman, then called to Gibbie who had been investigating the place where the big barn had stood.

Two heights of land distinguished the Notch Road. The first, near the Devil's Footprints, I had been aware of passing yesterday; the second had somehow escaped my attention. Now, retracing my steps, I knew when the second was reached. It was marked by a small sign nailed well up on a tree. There were so few signs anywhere along the road that meeting up with one gave me a friendly feeling.

When the road ran downhill I ran with it, passing Jerry Hall's still where once a man could bring his excess of grain and potatoes and receive in exchange a credible whiskey.

I paused at the site of the Carter Mill, where the

level had been raised by planks so water fell into
a "tub wheel" that powered an up-and-down saw.
Here logs were turned into boards and battens with
which the Notch houses were built; shingles were in
such good supply that they were sold at the Center
for three dollars a thousand. I thought of the logs
that came here, once great trees four to six feet in
diameter and more than two hundred feet high, and
of the men who had felled them. The twin grand-
sons, Charles and James, of that same James Bryant

who had perished in the blizzard, were famous choppers, perhaps the most famous in the Notch. Men of strength they were as well as skill; it was said that each one could place his blow where it counted. Getting into the woods at daybreak and not leaving till their stint was finished, they figured to cut each his three cords a day. They were men of business too, for they worked only by contract.

Near where the mill had stood was a spring, round and lined by blocks of granite that had gathered moss through the years. Ferns bent over the edge, oxalis trailed its heart-shaped leaves along the brink. If two people stood one on either side and reached across the water, their hands could have linked. At my approach a frog jumped in and disappeared, leaving scarcely a ripple. I knelt down and filled my cup. The water was cold, its taste delicious: vintage of Eden.

From here it was only a short distance to the Gilman place and the lane where Jonathan Gilman, returning by horse from a journey, would shout to his wife "Woman, I'm here!" and Sally came running to let down the bars and welcome him home. Perhaps he had some pretties in his pocket for Sally and the five children. It would have been like him.

As a young man, Jonathan Gilman had left the

Notch and endeavored to find a place in the world,
first as a farmer, then as a law student, a shoemaker,
a soldier, a mill-man. A friend reminded him that a
rolling stone gathers no moss and Jonathan must
have been in full agreement for he returned to the
Notch to marry Sally Dinsmore and take up farming

Spring near
Carter Mill

in earnest. She was hard-working; it was said that she
could help her husband roll logs at the mill as read-
ily as she could help him hoe a field of Indian corn.
The Gilman farm became known as one of the most
prosperous in the Notch.

In the small and peaceful burying place at Mount
Delight I had stood beside their graves. She had
outlived him by only two years and I could imagine

her waiting impatiently to hear the familiar shout "Woman, I'm here!" from the other side of time. When she heard it, how she must have run, shaking off her ninety-one years as if they were of no moment.

"Believe what you like," my friend of yesterday might have said to me.

There was another kind of story at the place where Mark Sargent built his log cabin, later on his house and barn of boards. He had a sharp-tongued wife who was thought by many to be a witch. Neighbors remembered hearing her say that she was going to buy Mark a hemlock coffin "so's he could go snapping through Hell." She lived to be a hundred and four, seeing far more years than he did, and probably she mellowed with time. One pleasure they had shared was seeing their daughter Mary marrying one of the Wallaces and standing up every inch a bride with her veil of mosquito netting.

The Wallaces were among the settlers from Scotland, and they had been the first to call the area Mount Delight. Many felt that the name harked back to a place of the same name in the Highlands, but continuing search revealed no such link. Not even the Director of Place-Name Survey in the School of Scottish Studies in Edinburgh has been able to find a Mount Delight in the Highlands or the

Lowlands, though there are Mount Joys and Mount
Pleasants.

I wished now that I had asked my friend the ori-
gin of the name, but even without asking I could
hear her answer. "Only a bonny place could have
a bonny name," she would have said. "There was no
other name for it, so highly pleased were they when
they saw it."

Yesterday, intent upon my journey, I had not
stopped to measure my foot in the Devil's. Crest-
ing the long hill that leveled at the height of land, I
saw the familiar landmark on my right. More than
one footprint had been depressed in the stone and
when the Devil did it he must have been on the run.
My own foot fitted comfortably into the print. I was
not surprised, remembering I had been told that
most people's did. I sat down on the sloping stone.

Directly across the width of road was a rock,
smooth-sided and higher than a man. Carved into
it, weather-worn but still legible, were the words:

P. Wentworths   6 mls.

1838

That must have been welcome information for a
traveler coming from the west. It meant that food
and drink, as well as other necessities, could soon be

Devil's footprints

purchased at the Wentworth store at Sandwich Lower Corner, and six miles must have seemed that the journey was near its end. P. Wentworth was an entrepreneur of the first order, one of the men who made Sandwich known as a place of "considerable trade" in the early years of the nineteenth century. He had business dealings up and down the Notch with farmers and at the sawmill; those with Jerry Hall at his still brightened his reputation.

What did Pastor Meader do with the Devil's Footprints? Took superstition away, most likely, and opened the minds of his listeners to the marvel of fact. His was no wordy theology, no Deity with ways inscrutable, but lessons people could read for them-

selves and take into their lives if they so desired.
Lava, flowing and cooling ages ago into a similitude
of footprints, took due from the Devil but gave honor
to natural forces. Explaining this, in his forthright
Quaker way, he might have added that there were
forces ever at work on men during their time on
earth.

Gibbie nudged me. I took the hint and started on
the road again.

THE ANSWER

COMING TO Beede's Falls, I turned off the road
and went through the small parking place, following the path to the river.

The day was still as gray and gentle as it had been
when I set out, but it was no longer silent. Ahead of
me was the purling of water as the Bearcamp slipped
over ledges and around rocks. Conscious of a powerful odor, I stopped, trying to decide what it was. Gibbie looked up at me. His nose was working but he
quite clearly preferred to stay by me rather than race
off in pursuit. Mink, I decided, or fisher; only a
predator leaves such an odor on the air.

The sound of the water became more musical. It
was running narrow in many places, but I crossed
and recrossed it; then found a pool from which to
drink and dipped my cup into it. Whittier's lines
came to mind—

> *To drink the wine of mountain air*
> *Beside the Bearcamp water.*

Beede's Falls

But I made a change in them for this was woodland wine, this Bearcamp water, wine chill and choice. Gibbie, downstream, was refreshing himself too.

I saw a perfect place to sit. It was at the base of a hemlock whose roots were like the arms of a chair. Here I would stay, listening to the flowing of water with my thoughts on the flowing of time. The sound was murmurous, like people talking together. Lovers talking, I corrected myself, as the girl at the pond would most certainly have done. Many must have come here during the years. Perhaps, if I looked, I would find some initials cut in the rocks. It could be that I would recognize whose they were, for the Notch people were becoming familiar to me.

Noon it might well be by now, for I was hungry and it felt good to sit down. The miles covered were not nearly so many as the years traveled back into the past and I still felt closer to the Notch life than to my own. Such a simple stalwart life it had been, in contrast to the present that is so rootless and rest-less. Master Ladd, you who had a molding influence on the thoughts of others, what would you say to young people today? Doctor Harris, what remedy would you prescribe for our ills? Pastor Meader, per-haps more than all else we need your call to inner quiet.

Opening my rucksack, I took out a hefty sandwich, a piece of cake, a banana, and two biscuits
for Gibbie. My thermos had been filled with cold
milk. In the woods behind me and across the stream
birds were chirping, fluttering among the branches.
Songless at this time of year, they were choristers
nonetheless to grace my meridian meal.

After eating, I rinsed my thermos and filled it
with water. I made myself comfortable in the hemlock chair, took the maps out and spread them beside me on the moss, then tried to bring my thinking into some kind of focus. The geological history
of the area had been long and violent, the human
history relatively brief; but there was a distillation
here of what had been an early way of life.

A primitive struggle had been waged for a hundred years or so and lost, some might say; but a
longer view might see it differently. Land never
adapted to farming had been wrested from the forest; its fertility served two or three generations, then
the forest quietly took it back again. A lesson learned
the hard way has become one of the principles of
present-day ecology.

When the first settlers came up into the Notch,
each one to clear and claim and work the hundred
acres granted him by the proprietors, the area must

have seemed hostile; but the hostility could be grappled with. A man measured his strength, his wit, his skill against it. There was danger on every side, there was work from daybreak to day's end; but with a clearing made, a cabin built, a woman beside him, roots were struck down in earth that was both home and wealth. Subdued and used, the land was not ravaged or violated. Needs were simple, wants few, and most of both were supplied from nearby field and adjacent forest. There was no lack of labor, for a home was a partnership in which its members shared. Responsibility came early and continued through life. Children had duties that grew as they did; old people had tasks that took into account their diminishing powers. And because the duties and the tasks needed to be done, each had the satisfaction of accomplishment.

In practically every house, for lengthening periods of time, three generations were under one roof. Incomprehensible it would have seemed to put older folk off by themselves. Barring illness physical or mental, they were still a part of the family, not apart. Without them, who would have pared the apples or wound the wool or cared for the babies? Who would have told stories to the little ones? Birth, growing, aging, death: that was the pattern. Within it were

joy and sorrow, success and failure, loneliness, rebellion, beauty and acceptance. Some households
might seem to have had more of one than another,
but if totals were added they would have shown that
every household had its share.

Time had its pattern too, but it was without pressure. It moved at a reasonable pace. A man did in a
day what a day could hold, his strength could take,
his animals endure. If more time was needed, work
could be resumed the next morning when the sun
came over the mountains and into the Notch. Time
turned with the seasons: spring with surge of new-
ness, plowing and planting; summer with growing
and reaping; fall with harvest in fields and orchards;
winter with weather that made for inwardness. But
with wood cut and seasoned, food stored for stock
and household, a family could sit out the weather.
Physical survival depended on work for three seasons; the fourth season gave another kind of test.
Again it was harder on some than on others, hardest
of all on the women.

But the Notch was a neighborhood. People must
have broken through the snow or traveled over it to
be with each other in need or fellowship. The loneliness that might have engulfed them could not com-
pare to the loneliness there is now in cities where too

many people do not know of each others' existence, or care.

A part of me yearned for that simpler way of living, while a part of me knew that there was no return.

Time flows as the river was flowing. I had gone from the *here* of my generation to the *there* of another century, and I had returned. In the journey my imagining might have been more romantic than realistic, but there must have been a measure of accuracy. At my point in time I could have the flavor of both worlds, and this was something impossible for the Notch people. There was no way they could have projected themselves into my present. Even the prodigious amounts of rum they drank could not have given them a glimpse. Had it, the effect would have been sobering.

What would they have thought of the speed with which life moves? of the callousness created by machines? of the frenzy with which people throw themselves into causes when for them just to live was cause enough?

The word *instant* was not in their vocabularies, except in the Biblical sense. They would have laughed at it, knowing that everything had its time of growing, maturing. They would have scorned the

thought of labor-saving devices, knowing all too well
that nothing was achieved without hard work. Men
and women constantly on the move would have puz-
zled them, for they had roots in the land and to it
they belonged.

Living in the Notch as I had for two days, traveling a road that led back as well as forward, I had felt
close to its people; but there was no escaping the fact
that I was a product of the present, heir to the past,
builder of the future, exactly as they were in their
day. Surrounded by comforts undreamed of to them,
my era had problems that would have been beyond
their comprehension.

Every age has a challenge for the pioneer: theirs
came in an economy of simplicity and hard work,
ours in an economy of affluence and a hurrying
tempo. But the challenge remains: to find the way
that is right and good for oneself and in relation to
others. Because of the very technology that has
brought such ease into our lives, we are in danger
of being alienated from our age-old and natural en-
vironment, the earth that has been man's home for
a long time. We are in danger of being cut off as
surely as some ethnic groups have been cut off, de-
liberately or voluntarily, from their pasts—with re-
sults that have been slow to appear, and sorrowful.

In the Greek myth, Antaeus lost his strength when he lost his touch with the earth.

We can still use the term *forefathers,* for there is only the sweep of a century between our time and the time when the interdependence of man and nature was the underpinning to life. As Notch folk read their Bibles, or took a cue from Pastor Meader when he read to them or spoke out of long familiarity with Scripture, I like to think that a different emphasis was put on the word *dominion* in the first chapter of Genesis. Even without conscious intent, they well might have understood the word to mean *stewardship.* Living close to the earth and dependent on it, they knew that if its waters, plants, creatures were not cared for, they themselves would be the losers.

Leaning back against the hemlock I closed my eyes, beginning to feel at peace with myself and the world in which I lived. I don't know what I had expected to find in the Notch, but I knew now that something of the old assurances by which men measure their lives had caught up with me.

The murmuring sound of the water went on as it had as long as water had flowed over that granite course. I could not get away from the feeling that it was the sound of lovers talking, a tender sound as if

all there was to be said would never be said as long
as time lasted. Man in love with the earth that is his
home, I thought; man, aware of his roots in the earth
and conscious of his identity with it and so with all
men everywhere. This is the reality before us today,
its reach made possible by the technology that has,
at the same time, given us problems to solve. As I
hugged my present to me, I felt glad for it.

What would Master Ladd say about the scope and
availability of education? And Doctor Harris about
the cures that are now commonplace for ills before
which he was helpless? Pastor Meader, you would indeed be gratified at the way religion has grown away
from ritual into social consciousness, moral responsibility. Yet the positive aspects of the present for
which I was glad would not exist at all were it not
for men such as these three.

Gibbie had been sleeping within reach of my out-
stretched hand; now I felt him alert. Lifting his head
and looking in the direction we had come from, he
made a low sound in his throat; then he left me. I
saw him leap the water and go toward the path, tail
wagging, barking gaily. It was not a bear, I decided.
Had it been he would not have left me. His tail
would have curved over his back, his hackle would
have risen, and his throaty growl would have clearly

said, "Come no nearer." It was not a fox or he would have gone off in gallant chase and soon returned, pleased with himself for having had an adventure on his own.

Then I saw them, walking hand in hand, a young man with crisp dark hair curling about his ears, a

young girl with short fair hair that was wind-tossed and charming. They wore the accouterments of hikers but their clothes looked new, not yet trail- and weather-tested. Gibbie stood before them asking for recognition. They gave it to him as if they knew something about dogs and their delights.

When they saw me, the man called out a hello. "We really didn't expect to see anyone here."

I was more surprised than they were. Indeed, I
would have been less surprised if someone out of the
Notch life had appeared, speaking with a slight burr
and wearing homespun clothes. But they were not
out of the nineteenth century; clearly they belonged
to the twentieth. It was Gibbie and his response to
them that shook me out of my revery.

"Hello," I replied. "It's good to see someone here
at Beede's Falls. I haven't seen anyone all day."

The girl smiled, "We haven't seen anyone since
we had our lunch in Wolfeboro, and that must have
been an hour ago."

They stepped over the stream, running narrow at
that point, to stand by my side.

I took my cup from its hitch on my belt and
handed it to the girl. "Thirsty? Even if you're not,
you should have a taste of Bearcamp water."

"Is it all right to drink?"

My nod must have given it good rating for she
took the cup from me and knelt to fill it with water.
"Thanks. I really am thirsty. It seems as if we've
been on the road a long time."

"I'm Sam Jones and this is my wife, Jennifer," the
young man said, holding out his hand to me.

I responded with my name and we sealed our ac-
quaintance with a handclasp.

"How did you get here? I didn't see your car at the parking space."

"I'm walking."

"Walking!" Now he was the one to look surprised.

"If this is water, I guess I've never tasted any before." Jennifer handed the cup to Sam. "Try it. It— it— well, it's like wine or something."

Then she and I shook hands.

"It comes from springs deep in the earth about a mile or more back in the woods," I told her. "At the source it's icy cold, even in the summer."

She looked at me with the wide wondering eyes of a child being told a story that might or might not be true, but strict truth did not matter because it was a good story.

He returned my cup. "Thanks, that was a treat, and needed." Catching sight of my Notch Road map lying open on the ground, he asked if he might look at it.

"Please do."

"We're on our way to Waterville Valley looking for some good fishing."

I told him the names of some of the ponds in the Notch.

"Maybe we won't have time to try more than one. We've got to be back in New York tomorrow."

After two days of timelessness, my encounter with the present was typical.

"You live in New York?"

"Yes, if you can call it living."

"Trapped is what he means," Jennifer explained; "that's what cities do to people these days." With a lithe motion, she crossed her legs at the ankles and sat down near me.

He sat down beside her and went on studying the map. "Jennie's right. And the senseless thing is that you can have your work there, and your home—if an apartment is a home—and never feel as if you belonged."

They could take my silence as agreement.

Satisfying himself as to where the ponds were in relation to the road and how they could be reached, he looked at the map more closely. "Do those numbers indicate houses? I didn't know there could be so many on an old dirt road. We took it because it looked like a short cut."

"It is a short cut, always has been, and those numbers don't indicate houses but cellar holes."

"Cellar holes!" Jennifer exclaimed. " What are they?"

"Places where a house once stood."

"We didn't see any."

"They're not all that evident, but you can generally find them by what grows near. Balm of Gilead trees are a sign, or a clump of lilacs, or a cinnamon rose bush trying to hold its own against the scrub, and apple trees. When you see them, you can be sure you're near where people once lived."

"Are you an archaeologist?" Sam asked.

"Oh, no——" I told them that I had been exploring the Notch with my dog, taking two days in which to do it.

Now they were sitting back to back, one leaning against the other and looking deliciously comfortable. Her fingers found their way over the moss to one of his hands; his other hand was resting lightly on Gibbie's back.

"Tell us about the Notch."

I did, the little I knew and the more I felt.

"——So the wild took it back again, easily because the land had never been ravaged or scarred. Coming in like a slow tide across the fields were daisies and devil's paintbrush and mullein, followed by blackberry and sumac, alder and hazel. They moved over the pastures preparing a way for the birches; then the pines came and among them some hardwoods, maple and beech, oak and ash. Trees took no notice of stone walls or barways, but moved up and over or

through them to the granite doorstones of houses,
casting seeds as they went.

"In only a little more time than it had taken to clear the land, the forest reclaimed it. Some of it has been owned and well managed by lumber companies since the turn of the century; some of it is included in the White Mountain National Forest; some of it is in private ownership. But now a great deal of it is in danger of commercial development."

The sound of water flowing followed my words, merging with them, carrying them along with it. Sam and Jennifer were so silent that I thought I had probably said more than I should. How could one expect two young people, urban and sophisticated, to care for this wilderness road with its aura of the past?

"What if it does get developed?" Sam asked. "There'll be a good road to get from Sandwich to Waterville Valley instead of going all around Squam Mountain, and that's the difference of ten miles against forty. There'll be access to probably some of the best fishing in the White Mountains. And the road's a natural for cross-country skiing."

"That's not all that could happen with development," I said, feeling just then as if I must be talking to myself.

"Correct." Sam had heard. "No one would want to see condominiums or a string of vacation homes rising in the Notch, I'll grant you that."

Jennifer made a quarter turn in her position and had her eyes fully on Sam.

"Well," he went on thoughtfully, "maybe it should be preserved as some sort of public recreation area. If that was done, there would have to be plenty of parking places along the road, and picnic tables, and lots of trash cans."

"And signs," Jennifer added.

"Yes, signs; all kinds of signs telling people what trails to take and not to litter and all that sort of thing." He paused. "That would change the character of the area almost as much as development."

To myself I said, Then you feel the Notch has character.

"One would be almost as bad as the other," Jennifer mused, reversing her quarter turn and resuming her back-to-back position with Sam. Her gaze was on the woodland across the Bearcamp. Her words, when she spoke, were not directed either to Sam or to me. "There's preservation for lots of different reasons: why shouldn't there be preservation for quiet? for walking? for gentleness?"

There was no need for either one of us to answer

her, for she was answering the Notch, or something that had been stirred in her by her being in the Notch.

"What if," she went on, venturing with her words, "what if the Notch were to be kept as it is, a wild and lovely place with its memories of a long ago time when a brave people lived in it and called it home?"

What if, I said to myself.

Sam picked up a hemlock cone and tossed it into the water. We followed its course with our eyes until the water swirled around a rock and the cone went from our view.

"Maybe that's the ideal solution," he said reluctantly. Then he turned to face his wife as if to compel her from a dream to reality. "But Jennie, what would people *do* here?"

"Just what we're doing. Being. Feeling something about another way of life, a hard but beautiful way. Oh Sam, think what those Notch people meant to each other! They were never just faces in a crowd as so many people are today. Each one was a human being with a name, and somehow or another each one counted."

Sam shook his head slowly, thoughtfully, but when he spoke it was to me and he said that he guessed I probably agreed with Jennifer.

"I do."

"Why?"

"Because I think there should be room in every-one's life for just what the Notch has—quiet and great trees, running water and memories, and a road that can draw a person into the past as well as get from Sandwich to Campton."

"Lots of people think they're getting back to the past by wearing sandals and trying to grow their own food," Jennifer suggested.

"Gestures!" Sam shrugged his shoulders. "I doubt if they get very far unless the ancient verities go along with the old clothes."

"The ancient verities." She rolled the words around as if she liked the sound of them, smiling as she did so.

"I'm an engineer," Sam said to me, "and I work more with machines than people, but I'm beginning to see something. It just may be that the more our lives become mechanized the more we are going to need places where we can hark back to our original dependence on the land. Perhaps we don't need recreation so much as re-creation."

I nodded, thinking of the change made in a word's meaning by accent and emphasis.

Jennifer gave a happy little sigh, as if she had

known all along that Sam would come up with a
solution.

Sam, obviously on the way to agreement with his wife and me, had more to say. "Maybe it sounds far-fetched, but the Notch with its day makes me think of Greek civilization with its. Both went out, but both left a heritage. The Greek wasn't entirely lost, nor should the Notch be."

"But there's no art here," Jennifer exclaimed in surprise, "or writing, or buildings, or——"

"No, but there's simplicity, hard work, kinship with the earth. That's enough of a heritage; and what's more it's ours."

Her admiration was in the smile she gave him. "I never thought I was a flag-waver, but Sam, you make me proud to be part of America."

The easiest thing for them both to do, and probably the only response each could make to the other, was a kiss.

When Sam stood up he gave her his hand. She was too nimble really to need it, but she took it and saw no reason to let it go.

"I think we'll try Kiah Pond," he said. "Maybe we'll get a few of those red trout."

They thanked me for what information I had given them and for my cup from which they had both drunk. They said they were glad they had stumbled on me in a place where they had not thought to find anyone.

"We're newlyweds," Sam explained, "and we just had this week to discover New Hampshire."

And your lives to discover each other, I thought. "Congratulations, and the best of everything including the fishing."

They turned to go. Gibbie watched them, his tail wagging as a dog's will when a meeting has been pleasant and the feel of it lingers. I watched them too, until they were out of sight. Her arm was around his waist, his hand rested on her shoulder, reaching up now and then to tousle her hair. The forest near Beede's Falls and the Bearcamp River had seen many lovers. It would see more.

"It's yours——" the girl at the pond had said to me. "It's ours——" the young husband had said. Her words somehow carried responsibility; his, ownership by discovery. My own feeling embraced both, underscored by the conviction that unless we keep our link with the past, our contact with the earth, we are in danger of losing ourselves. We, the people of the present, may be in a greater predicament than the natural areas we are trying to save.

Gibbie pushed himself against me. His ears were

laid back, his tail moved slowly, his gaze was earnest.
It was his way of communication; over the years I
had learned to interpret it. "All right, we'll go."

I folded the map and put it away, slung the ruck-sack over my shoulders and stood up. Gibbie barked excitedly and capered around me. With neither sun in the sky nor watch on my wrist, I had no way of knowing the hour, but I could trust Gibbie's sense of time. There were still a few miles to do before we got out of the Notch and in to Center Sandwich. It would be well to do them in daylight.

The time, or perhaps its exigency, reminded me of one of the stories I had been told about two Notch people fishing on one of the Hall ponds. Still fishing as night came down, they turned toward shore and rowed as hard as they could. One said to the other, "We must get out as quick as God will let us."

The measurement of hours had been no part of my two days, and distance had been the length of a road and its environs. In my thermos was water from the Bearcamp, in my pocket a piece of brick from a crumbling chimney, in my heart a deep quiet. Trudging along the road, I found myself singing a song we campers had loved in that faraway time when I had spent a memorable summer in the shadow of the White Mountains—

Seven miles of sandy road,
Seven miles of stone,
Summer's almost gone,
Summer's almost gone.

Time was running out in more ways than one.

At the fork where the Notch Road joined the Diamond Ledge Road, I paused. There was the sign on the tree which had pointed my way the previous morning. Turning around for one last view of the road winding its way through the forest, I thought of the controversy that had marked its beginning nearly a hundred and seventy-five years ago; but it had proved bigger than controversy and had survived. I had faith that it could surmount the present controversy and survive. Dear shades moved among the shadows, chief of them Moses Hall, that self-appointed guardian and host. I raised my hand in salutation.

The rise of the road before me was gradual until it leveled at the first opening in the trees, thereafter it would run downhill. Here were pastures with cattle still grazing, and green fields that sloped toward Squam Lake, its waters flat-surfaced and gray. On one side was the rounded shape of Red Hill, only a little darker than the sky that was darkening to twi-

light. That was the hill Daniel Beede had climbed so
long ago to see the grants which he would be among
the first to settle. From it he had looked down on
a land of lakes in a forest wilderness, rimmed by
mountains. In his mind's eye he might have beheld
clearings and cabins linked by trails.

From Red Hill today the view is little different.
The lakes, the woodland, the mountains are there,
but the settlements have become villages with white
houses and church spires. Instead of trails there are

roads linking house to house, village to village, and so to towns and the rest of the world. Three thousand miles due west was the Cascade Range, that primitive wilderness which had only recently and not without controversy been saved for people to enjoy and in which to re-create themselves. Tiny as Sandwich Notch might be in comparison, it and the Cascades have kinship: they are ours to cherish as long as trees grow and waters flow.

Why save Sandwich Notch? The question that brought me to it was answered by the road itself.

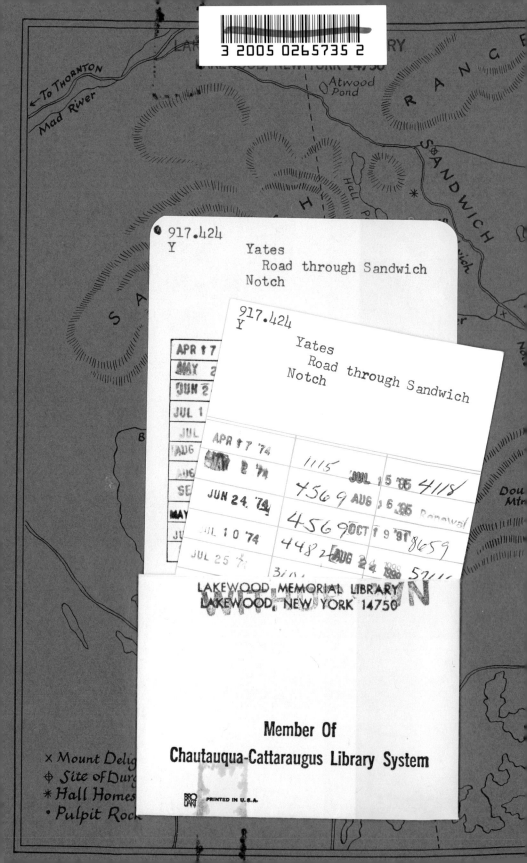